D0307026

WINDOWS® 95 FOR BEGINNERS

Gillian Doherty

Edited by Philippa Wingate

Designed by Russell Punter and Neil Francis
Illustrated by Bill Greenhead
Photography by Howard Allman

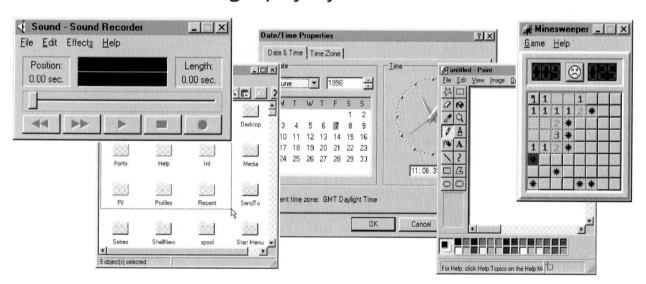

Technical consultant: Nigel Peet
Series editor: Jane Chisholm

Contents

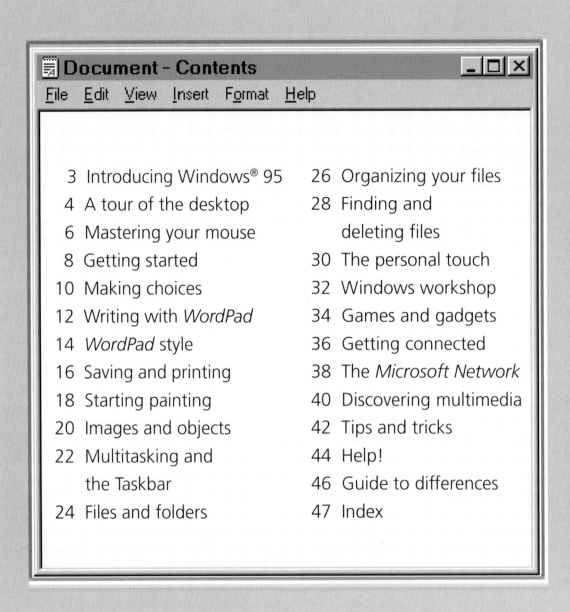

Introducing Windows® 95

This book will provide you with all the information you need to get started with Microsoft® Windows® 95. You can also find out how to use the programs supplied with Windows 95.

What is Windows?

Windows 95 is a special kind of program called an operating system. An operating system controls your computer. It enables you to use other programs and tell your computer what to do.

With Windows, you work with pictures called graphics. You can use these to give the computer instructions.

What's new in 95?

Windows 95 is the latest version of Windows. The previous versions include Windows 3.1, Windows 3.11 and Windows for Workgroups. The new features and improvements are intended to make using your computer easier than ever.

If you already have Windows on your computer, you only need to buy the Windows 95 Upgrade pack. When you put this on your computer, it is added over your existing version of Windows. This

means that you keep any programs that are already on your computer. The way that your programs are organized will also stay the same, making it easy for you to find things.

There is a section on page 46 for anybody who has used a previous version of Windows. This guides you through some of the main differences with Windows 95 and helps you to look up the new ways of carrying out certain tasks.

Windows 95 Upgrade

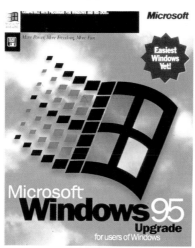

What do you need?

For most of the things you will do in this book, all you need is the Windows 95 software.

We have assumed that you already have Windows 95 on your computer. If you don't, you will need to put it on, or install it. When you buy Windows 95, it comes with instructions telling you how to do this.

What next?

If you are just starting to use Windows 95, you should work your way through this book from the beginning and follow what is happening on your computer at the same time. This will help you to become familiar with the basics of Windows 95.

If you want to know how to do something specific, turn to the index at the end of the book to see where you can find out about it.

Solving problems

If you get stuck, Windows 95 has its own help system. Turn to page 44 to find out how to use it.

Throughout this book there are warning boxes containing the symbol shown below. These are to alert you to problems that you might come across and give you hints for avoiding or solving them.

Warning symbol

A tour of the desktop

This section tells you how to start Windows 95 and guides you through some of the first things you'll see on your screen. You'll also receive a tour of the Windows 95 desktop and find out about the items on it.

Ready, steady, go

Windows 95 starts automatically when you switch on your computer. After a few seconds, the message **Starting Windows 95** will appear.

It takes Windows 95 about a minute to start up. During this time, you may see several pages of text flash onto your screen. You will also see a picture of a tiny egg-timer. This means that Windows 95 is busy starting up. While you are waiting, a screen like the one below will be displayed.

The Windows 95 opening screen

The desktop

After the opening screen of Windows 95, a coloured or patterned display called the desktop will appear. It contains several small pictures, called icons, which each represent a particular program.

The desktop is the area where you use the programs on your computer. Like a real desk, the Windows 95 desktop is a workspace containing lots of different tools to help you work.

The picture below shows some of the things you can expect to find on your desktop. Don't worry if it doesn't show the same icons as this one; some computers have different programs.

My Computer
This icon allows you to look at what information is stored on your computer. Find out about it on page 24.

Recycle Bin
When you no longer need a document, you can throw it into the *Recycle Bin*. Find out how to use it on page 28.

My Briefcase
If you sometimes work on different computers, this program helps you to keep them up-to-date. Find out how to use it on page 36.

Network Neighborhood
This program will help you if your computer is connected to other computers. Find out about it on page 37.

The Microsoft Network
This icon enables you to connect your computer to Microsoft's information service. Find out more about it on page 38.

Inbox
This program enables you to create, send, and receive electronic mail. Find out more about it on page 39.

Start button
The Start button provides you with access to almost everything you need to use in Windows 95. Find out about it on page 8.

4

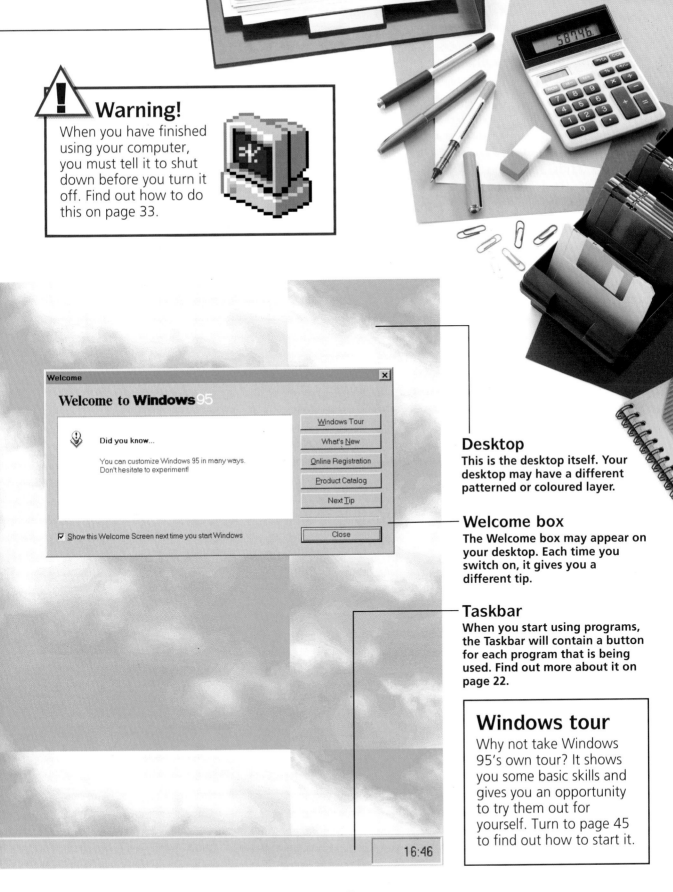

⚠ Warning!

When you have finished using your computer, you must tell it to shut down before you turn it off. Find out how to do this on page 33.

Welcome to **Windows** 95

Did you know...

You can customize Windows 95 in many ways. Don't hesitate to experiment!

☑ Show this Welcome Screen next time you start Windows

- Windows Tour
- What's New
- Online Registration
- Product Catalog
- Next Tip
- Close

16:46

Desktop

This is the desktop itself. Your desktop may have a different patterned or coloured layer.

Welcome box

The Welcome box may appear on your desktop. Each time you switch on, it gives you a different tip.

Taskbar

When you start using programs, the Taskbar will contain a button for each program that is being used. Find out more about it on page 22.

Windows tour

Why not take Windows 95's own tour? It shows you some basic skills and gives you an opportunity to try them out for yourself. Turn to page 45 to find out how to start it.

Mastering your mouse

One of the most important tools you will need to use Windows 95 effectively is a mouse. Windows 95 uses pictures to present information and you give your computer instructions by "touching" these pictures using a mouse.

On these pages, you'll find out about the different ways in which you can use a mouse to make things happen.

This device is called a mouse because of its shape and long tail-like cable.

Moving your mouse

When you move your mouse around on a flat surface, it sends signals to a pointer on the screen. This pointer follows the movements of your mouse.

Try pointing at the different icons on the desktop by moving the mouse until the tip of the pointer is positioned over an icon.

Pointing at an icon

Some computers have a device called a touchpad instead of a mouse. You use a touchpad by moving your finger across its surface.

A computer with touchpad

Touchpad

Pointer power

The main pointer symbol you'll come across is this simple arrow.

 Arrow pointer

As you move the pointer around the display, you will notice that it sometimes changes shape. It changes according to the tasks for which you can use it. Here are some of the different shaped pointers you may see.

Pointer symbols

      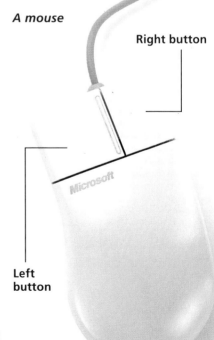

Mouse buttons

In order to touch the items on your display, you need to press the buttons on your mouse. There are two main ways of touching things: clicking and double-clicking.

Throughout this book, whenever you are told to click on something, you should use the left mouse button, unless the right mouse button is specified. The picture below shows which mouse button is which. If a mouse has more than two buttons, it is the outer buttons that are important.

A mouse

Right button

Left button

6

Clicking

You can touch, or click on, icons and certain parts of your display by pointing at them and pressing and releasing a mouse button. Clicking on items in this way gives your computer information.

Try clicking once on the *My Computer* icon. The icon will change colour. You have now selected it. This means that you have told the computer that you want to do something to the icon. To deselect the icon, click on a blank part of the desktop.

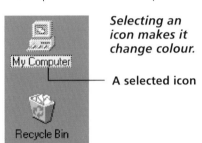

Selecting an icon makes it change colour.

— **A selected icon**

If you still have a Welcome box on your desktop (see page 5), you can close it by clicking once on the cross in the top right-hand corner of the box.

Double-clicking

Double-clicking means pressing a mouse button twice very quickly. It usually offers a shortcut to carrying out a particular task.

Try double-clicking on the *My Computer* icon. A box containing several icons will appear on your desktop. Close it by clicking once on the cross in the top right-hand corner.

Close button

The right button

The right mouse button also allows you to take shortcuts.

Try clicking on the *My Computer* icon with the right mouse button. A list like the one below will appear. Click on a blank part of the desktop to make the list disappear.

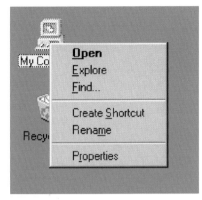

Clicking with the right mouse button opens a list like this one.

You'll find out more about what the right button allows you to do later in the book.

Dragging

To move things around on your desktop you need to use a technique called dragging. Try pointing at the *My Computer* icon again. Press and hold down the left mouse button. Keeping the button pressed, move your mouse. The icon on the screen will move too.

When you have finished dragging an object, release the mouse button to drop it.

Now try dragging an icon with the right mouse button pressed instead of the left button. When you release it, a menu will appear. To get rid of the menu, click on the desktop with the left button.

Dragging an icon

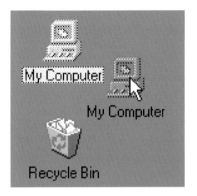

Mouse trouble

Are you left-handed? Your mouse is probably prepared for a right-handed user, which means that you may find it a little awkward to use. To find out how to make it suitable for a left-handed user, see page 42.

Beware! The instructions in this book are for a right-handed mouse. If you do change the way your mouse works, your left and right mouse buttons will swap roles.

Getting started

The Start button is the place where you will begin most of the things you want to do in Windows 95. You can use it to start, or launch, a program. Each program appears on your desktop in a box called a window. On these pages you will find out about the main parts of a window.

Starting up

The Start button is positioned at the end of the Taskbar. If you rest your pointer over it for a few seconds, a message which reads **Click here to begin** will appear.

The Start button ————

Try clicking on the Start button. A list, called a menu, opens. Some of the items on the menu have arrowheads beside them. When you select one of these items, by resting your pointer over it for a second, another menu will open.

Menus opening out from the Start button

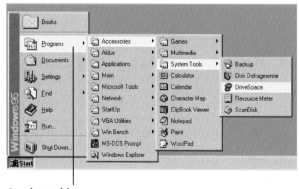

A selected item

Launching a program

Now try launching a program called *WordPad*. To do this, select the word *Programs* from the first menu above the Start button. The menu that opens contains the names of collections of programs, called program groups. *WordPad* is usually in a program group called *Accessories*. To launch the *WordPad* program, simply click on its name. It will appear in a window on your desktop.

What is a window?

A window is a rectangular space in which you work with a particular program. When a program is running in a window, the window is said to be open.

The screen below shows a typical window and names some of its main parts.

A WordPad window

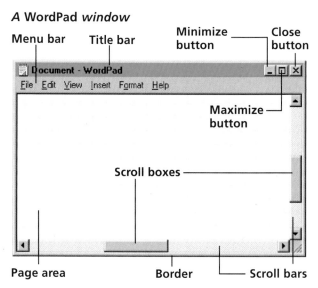

Maximizing and restoring

To take a closer look at a window, you can enlarge it by clicking on its Maximize button. When a window is maximized, it fills the whole screen so that you can't see its border. Its Maximize button disappears and is replaced by a Restore button. When you click on the Restore button, the window will return to its original size and position on your desktop.

When a window isn't maximized, you can still see the desktop.

A maximized window fills the entire desktop.

A Maximize button

A Restore button

Minimizing

When you are not using a window, you can clear it off your desktop by reducing it to an icon. To do this, click on its Minimize button. This shrinks the window so that it only appears as a button on the Taskbar. The program is still running, but it is tucked out of the way.

When you want to enlarge the window again, click on the button that represents the program on the Taskbar and it will return to its previous size and position.

A Minimize button

A program button

Resizing a window

As long as a window hasn't been maximized, you can alter its size and shape. To do this, move the pointer over the border of the window. It will change to a double-headed arrow. If you hold down the left mouse button and drag the border, you can change the height and width of the window. Release the mouse button when the window is the size you want.

A window can be stretched in different directions.

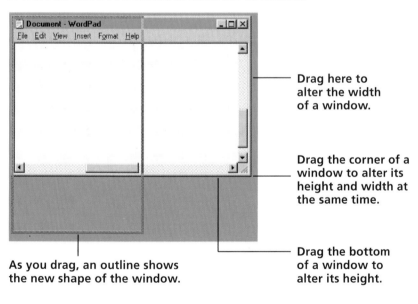

As you drag, an outline shows the new shape of the window.

Drag here to alter the width of a window.

Drag the corner of a window to alter its height and width at the same time.

Drag the bottom of a window to alter its height.

Scroll bars

The window below has scroll bars along its right and bottom edges. This tells you that it is too small to display all of its contents. Each scroll bar has a scroll box on it. Dragging a scroll box along a scroll bar allows you to look at different parts of the area inside a window. If you only want to move a little at a time, click on the arrowheads at either end of the scroll bar.

A window with scroll bars

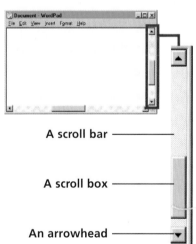

A scroll bar

A scroll box

An arrowhead

Moving a window

If a window hasn't been maximized, you can move it around your desktop. To do this, point at a blank part of its Title bar. Holding down the left mouse button, drag the window to a new location. Release the mouse button to drop the window into its new position.

Closing a window

When you have finished using a program, you can stop it running by closing its window. To do this, click on its Close button.

A Close button

Making choices

You can give your computer instructions by choosing from certain options inside a window. There are many different ways of doing this. On these pages, you will see some of the main ways.

Menu bar and menus

When you launch a program, you will see a Menu bar along the top of its window. Look at the *WordPad* window you opened on page 8 to see for yourself.

To open a menu, click on its name on the Menu bar. If you then move the pointer along the Menu bar, this opens the other menus one at a time. To close a menu, click on its name again or press the Esc key on your keyboard.

Opening a menu

A menu name

An open menu

Menu options

A menu contains a list of options. These options represent different kinds of instructions that you can give to your computer. You select an option by clicking on it.

You can use options to tell your computer to carry out certain tasks, such as printing out documents, or to switch on particular features on the display. Sometimes, when you select an option, you will be asked to give more information about your choice before a task can be carried out.

If an option is shown in light grey print, this tells you that it is not available. If you click on one of these options, nothing will happen.

Menu symbols

Some menu options have symbols beside them. The menu below shows what some of these symbols mean.

Different types of menu symbols

A tick beside an option means that it is switched on. Click on it to switch it off.

A dot indicates that an item is selected. Here you can choose any one of these four items.

Three dots after an option means more information is needed. (See the section on dialog boxes on page 11.)

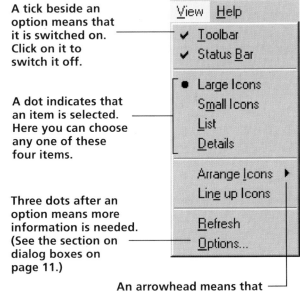

An arrowhead means that another menu will open up.

Keyboard commands

Some menu options have codes, called keyboard commands, beside them. This means that you can tell your computer what to do by simultaneously pressing the keys indicated by the code, instead of selecting the option with your mouse. Using keyboard commands can be a quicker way of giving instructions once you remember which keys to press.

Most keyboard commands include the Control, Alt or Shift keys, followed by a letter. For example, instead of selecting the *Print* option on *WordPad's File* menu, you can press the Control key and the letter P.

Alt key   Shift key   Control key

Dialog boxes

If you select a menu option that is followed by three dots, a box, called a dialog box, will open. You use this box to give the computer more information about your choice.

Completing a dialog box is like filling in a questionnaire. You are given several choices and your responses tell the computer exactly what you want to do.

Windows 95 has several different ways of letting you indicate your choices. The picture below shows some of the features you will find in dialog boxes.

An example dialog box

A Drop-down list box. Click on the arrowhead to open a list of options.

A List box. Select an option by clicking on its name. Use the scroll bar to see the rest of the list.

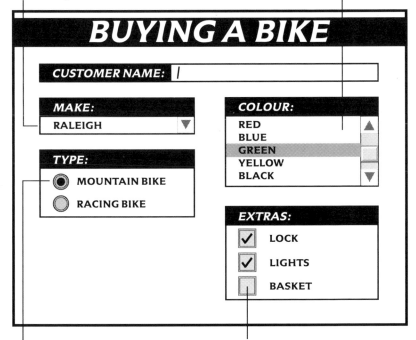

BUYING A BIKE

CUSTOMER NAME: |

MAKE:
RALEIGH ▼

TYPE:
◉ MOUNTAIN BIKE
○ RACING BIKE

COLOUR:
RED
BLUE
GREEN
YELLOW
BLACK
▲ ▼

EXTRAS:
☑ LOCK
☑ LIGHTS
☐ BASKET

An Option button. When you select an option like this, a black dot appears in the button next to it. Clicking on a different option switches the first one off.

A Check box. Click in a box to switch an option on or off. When an option is on, a tick appears in the box.

Dividers

Some dialog boxes are divided into different sections called property sheets. Each section is represented by a sheet with a tab at the top. To see an example, open *Control Panel* from the *Settings* menu on the Start menu. Double-click on the *Mouse* icon. The *Mouse Properties* dialog box shown below will appear.

The Mouse Properties *dialog box*

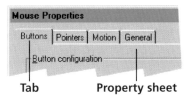

Tab   **Property sheet**

To look at the contents of a particular sheet, click on the relevant tab. Try looking at the *Pointers* sheet by clicking on its tab. Each sheet is like a separate dialog box.

Command buttons

All dialog boxes contain buttons. Many of them have commands such as *Save* or *Display* written on them. To use a command button, simply click on it.

A command button   Apply

The most common command buttons you will come across are *OK* and *Cancel* buttons. When you have finished making your selections in a dialog box, you can tell your computer to put the changes into effect by clicking on the *OK* button.

To close a dialog box without making any changes, click on its *Cancel* button.

Writing with *WordPad*

WordPad is a program which comes with Windows 95. You can use it to type in and organize text and to change the way the text looks. This is called word processing.

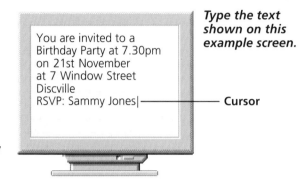

You are invited to a Birthday Party at 7.30pm on 21st November at 7 Window Street Discville RSVP: Sammy Jones|

Type the text shown on this example screen.

— Cursor

About *WordPad*

Launch *WordPad* from the *Accessories* menu by clicking on its name. Make sure its window is maximized so that you can see it clearly.

The WordPad *window*

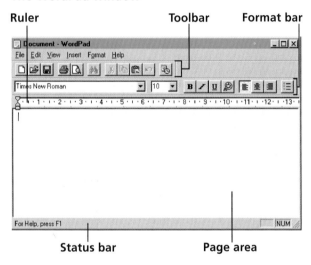

Ruler   Toolbar   Format bar

Status bar   Page area

The *WordPad* window above contains tools to help you to work with a text document. There is a Toolbar, Format bar, Ruler and Status bar. If any of these items is not shown in your *WordPad* window, you can switch it on by clicking on its name on the *View* menu.

Write on

When you launch *WordPad,* a flashing vertical line, called the cursor, appears in the top left-hand corner of the page area. This shows where text will appear when you start to type.

Try typing the text shown on the following example screen. As you type, the text automatically "wraps" onto the next line when it reaches the end of a line. If you want to make it start a new line yourself, you can do this by pressing the Return (or Enter) key.

Moving the cursor

When you move the pointer over the page area, it changes into an I-shaped pointer. You can use this to position the cursor. Before you can move it to an area of the page where there is no text, you'll need to use the Return key to move down the page. Then point to where you want the cursor to go and click with the mouse button. It jumps to the point where you clicked. When you start typing, the text will appear at that point.

I-shaped pointer   I

Selecting text

You can mark a section of text that you want to change by selecting it. To do this, position the pointer to the left of the text you want to select. Holding down the mouse button, drag the pointer to the end of the section. This highlights the text. You can deselect text by clicking elsewhere in the window.

Selected text   Party

⚠ Warning!

Be careful when you have selected text. Anything that you type will replace the text that is highlighted. If you replace something by mistake, stay calm! Clicking on the Undo button will make your selected text reappear.

Undo button

Deleting text

If you make a mistake when typing in text, you can correct it. Text is made up of letters, numbers and symbols called characters. The Delete key deletes the character to the right of the cursor and the Backspace key deletes the character to the left.

You can delete a whole section of text at once by selecting it and then pressing either the Delete or the Backspace key.

Backspace key   **Delete key**

Cut and paste

You can move sections of text from one part of a document to another. To do this, select the text you want to move and then click on the Cut button shown below. The selected text will disappear from the document. The text is actually moved to a special location called the Clipboard where it is stored.

Now position the cursor where you want to move the text and click on the Paste button. This pastes the text from the Clipboard into your document.

 Cut button

 Paste button

Copying text

You can use the Clipboard to copy text. Select the text you want to copy and then click on the Copy button shown below. The text remains where it is, but a copy of it is sent to the Clipboard. You can paste the copied text into another position in your document by clicking on the Paste button.   **Copy button**

Finding text

WordPad has a feature called *Find* which allows you to search for a particular word in your document. Click on the button shown on the right to open the *Find* dialog box.   **Find button**

Click in the *Find what* box and enter the word you are looking for. Use the check boxes to tell the computer exactly what to search for. Selecting *Match whole word only* tells the computer not to look for the word inside longer words. For example, if the word you typed was "invite", it would not look for words like "invited" and "invites". Selecting *Match case* tells the computer to look only for words that have the same capital and small letters.

Click on the *Find Next* button to start the search. The program searches for the first time the word occurs and highlights it.

The **Find** *dialog box*

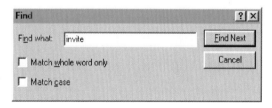

Replacing text

You can find and replace a particular word by selecting *Replace* from the *Edit* menu. Type the word you are looking for in the *Find what* box. Then type the word with which you want to replace it in the *Replace with* box. Click on the *Replace* button to search for and replace the next matching word, or *Replace All* to replace the word every time it occurs in your document.

WordPad style

WordPad has lots of tools for improving the way a document looks. You can use these tools to change the shape, position and style of your text.

Style choices

WordPad offers several different ways of changing the way text looks. You can alter the shape of the characters that make up your text by changing the "font". You can also change the size of the letters and choose from text styles such as underlined, *italic* or **bold**. Before you can change text in your document, you will need to select it (see page 12).

Click on the *Font* option on the *Format* menu to see the fonts and styles that are available. If you click on an option, the sample box shows how your text will look if you select that option. Click on *OK* when you have made your choices.

The Font *dialog box*

List of fonts   Style list   Font size list

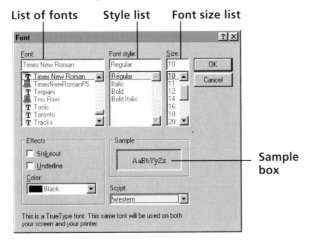

Sample box

The Format bar

The *WordPad* program includes a device called the Format bar. This offers an alternative way of changing the appearance of your text.

When you open *WordPad,* the Format bar should be displayed across the top of the window. If it isn't, turn to page 12 to find out how to switch it on.

Format buttons

The buttons and boxes on the Format bar offer quick ways of making some of the same changes you can make using the *Font* dialog box. To use one of these buttons, first highlight the text you want to change and then click on the button.

Use these buttons and boxes to change your text.

Choose a font from the drop-down list.   Change the font size in this box.

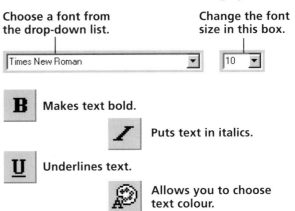

B   Makes text bold.

I   Puts text in italics.

U   Underlines text.

Allows you to choose text colour.

Positioning text

The buttons below allow you to change the position of your text on the page. This is called aligning the text. You can line it up with the left or right edge of the page, or position it between the two.

Buttons for positioning text

Lines text up against the left-hand side.   Positions text in the middle.   Lines text up against the right-hand side.

Page Setup

When you create a document in *WordPad*, you need to tell your computer what size page you want and where you want to position the text on the page. To do this, choose *Page Setup* from the *File* menu.

Use the *Size* drop-down list in the *Paper* section to tell the computer what size paper you are using to print out your document.

The Page Setup *dialog box*

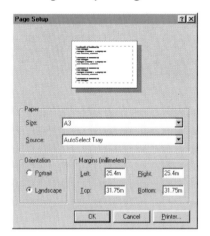

The *Portrait* and *Landscape* options allow you to choose between a vertical and a horizontal page setup.

These pictures show how the page will look.

Portrait   Landscape

Use the *Margins* section to tell your computer how much space to leave between the edge of the page and the edge of your text. To do this, simply click in a box and enter a new distance value.

Using the Ruler

You can use *WordPad*'s Ruler (see page 12) to help you arrange your text on the page.

When you press the Tab key on your keyboard, the cursor jumps a set distance. The Ruler can be used to change this distance. To see how this works, try clicking on the Ruler at several different points. L-shaped symbols, called tab stops, will appear at the points where you clicked.

When you press the Tab key on your keyboard, the cursor jumps so that it is in line with the next tab stop. When you start to type, the text will appear at that point.

You can move a tab stop by dragging it. To get rid of it entirely, drag it beyond the left edge of the Ruler.

Tab stops can help you to line up text.

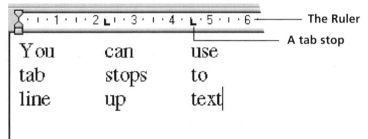

The Ruler
A tab stop

Be creative

Try using some of the tools and techniques you have read about to alter the invitation you typed on page 12. Here are some suggestions for things to try.

For an invitation, you could position the text in the middle of the page.

Put the heading in a large font and underline it.

Use bold to make important words stand out.

Saving and printing

When you have created a document, Windows 95 allows you to store it. This is called saving a document. You can also print out a copy on paper.

About disks

The main places you can store documents, or files, are your computer's hard disk and floppy disks. The hard disk is inside the computer and can store lots of information. Floppy disks are made of plastic and can be used to keep copies of your files, or to carry files to another computer.

The *Save As* box

When you save a file, you need to give it a name and tell your computer where to store it. In Windows 95 programs, you can do this by choosing the *Save As* option from the *File* menu.

If you try saving the *WordPad* document you created on page 15, a dialog box like the one below will appear on your desktop.

The Save As dialog box

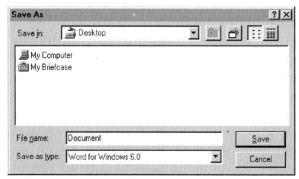

Naming a file

Click in the *File name* box to enter a name for your file. It can be up to 255 characters long and can include spaces but none of these characters: /*<>?":|

Always give files descriptive names so that you can remember what they contain. For example, save the *WordPad* document you created on page 15 using the name **WordPad Invitation**.

Where to save

Open the *Save in* drop down list in the *Save As* box. You use this to tell your computer where to store a file when it saves it. It probably contains icons for your disk drives, *My Briefcase, My Computer* and the desktop. The hard disk drive is normally labelled **C:**. In this book it is referred to as the C drive.

Saving a file

Now try saving WordPad Invitation. To do this, open the *Save in* drop-down list and click on the C drive icon. In the box below, select the icon with the word Windows beside it and click on the *Open* button. This tells your computer that you want to save WordPad Invitation in a place called the Windows folder on the C drive. This is only for temporary storage. Turn to page 26 to find out about organizing and storing documents.

Now click on the *Save* button. While the computer is saving the file, your pointer will change to an egg-timer. This tells you that the computer is busy carrying out an instruction.

The "busy" symbol

Existing files

If you type a file name that is the same as a file already on the disk, a message appears asking whether you want to replace the existing file with the one you are trying to save. Click on the *Yes* button to replace it, or click on *No* and then choose a different name for the file.

You only need to use the *Save As* command if you are saving a new file. If you have just changed an existing file, you can save it by clicking on the Save button.

Save button

16

Preparing to print

Before you can print out a file, you need to check that your computer and printer are properly connected and that you have loaded the printer with paper.

Your printer also needs to be switched on and "on-line", which means that it is ready to receive your printing instructions. Most printers have an on-line button with a light beside it to show when the printer is ready.

Print preview

Check that your document looks the way you want it to before you print it. Click on the Print Preview button to see the whole document at once.

Print Preview button

The *Print* box

You need to give your computer information about the kind of printer you are using and what you want it to print. In Windows 95 programs, you can do this by choosing the *Print* option from the *File* menu. This opens a *Print* dialog box like the one shown below.

In the *Printer* section, select the name of the printer you are using from the *Name* drop-down list.

The* Print *dialog box

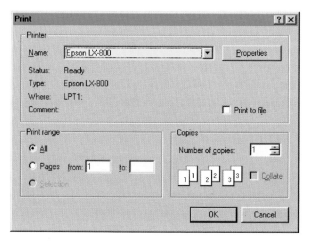

Which pages?

If a document has several pages, you can choose which ones you want to print in the *Print range* section of the *Print* dialog box. To print all of the pages, select *All*.

Number of copies

You can choose how many copies of your document you want to print in the *Copies* section of the *Print* dialog box. Click on the arrowheads to change the number of copies.

When you have entered all the print information, click on *OK* to start printing. A message confirming that your document is being printed will appear briefly in a box on your desktop.

Printing

When a file is being printed, you will see a printer icon at the end of the Taskbar. Double-click on it to open the *Print Manager* window.

Printer icon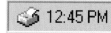

Your printer can only print one file at a time. If you try to print a second one, *Print Manager* holds it in a queue until the printer is ready. The *Print Manager* window shows the order in which files will be printed.

To cancel a print command, click on the name of the file you want to cancel with the right mouse button. Then, from the menu that appears, select *Cancel Printing*.

The* Print Manager *window

Starting painting

The Windows 95 package contains a program called *Paint,* which you can use to create pictures on your computer screen.

About *Paint*

Paint is usually found in the *Accessories* program group. Click on its name to launch it, and then maximize its window.

The *Paint* window below contains a colour palette and a collection of buttons called the Toolbox. These buttons represent drawing and painting tools.

The Paint *window*

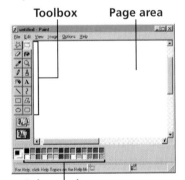

Toolbox   Page area

Colour palette

Selecting colours

Before you start drawing, you need to select the colours you want to use. Choose a background colour to draw on and a foreground colour to draw with.

To select a foreground colour, click on a colour from the palette with the left mouse button. Use the right mouse button to select a background colour.

Shape tools

The tools shown below enable you to draw different shapes.

Shape tools

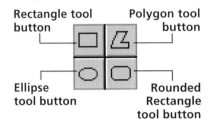

Rectangle tool button

Polygon tool button

Ellipse tool button

Rounded Rectangle tool button

To use a Shape tool, click on its button and move your pointer to where you want the shape to appear on the page. Keeping the left mouse button pressed, drag the mouse to create the shape you want.

You can use the Rectangle and Ellipse tools to create perfect squares and circles by holding down the Shift button while you drag a shape.

The Polygon tool enables you to create a shape with many sides. You use it by dragging out connected lines. Join the end of the last line to the start of the first line to create a closed shape.

When you select a shape tool, you can choose from the different methods of shading shown below.

Shading options

Draws outline of shape in foreground colour, with no shading

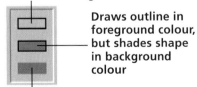

Draws outline in foreground colour, but shades shape in background colour

Draws and shades shape in background colour

Painting tools

There are several tools, shown below, that allow you to use different styles of drawing, painting and shading.

To select one of these tools, click on its button. Moving your mouse moves the tool on the screen. To draw with the tool, keep the mouse button pressed while you move the mouse around.

You can shade in a closed shape by selecting the Fill tool and then clicking on the area that you want to shade. This fills the shape with the foreground colour.

Drawing and painting tools

 Pencil tool button

 Brush tool button

 Airbrush tool button

 Fill tool button

Different strokes

You can change the width of the strokes made by some of the tools. If this option is available for a particular tool, when you select that tool a box displaying the different stroke widths will appear below the Toolbox. Click on the width you require.

Different stroke widths for the Brush tool

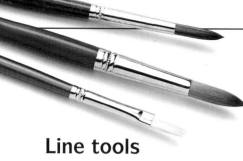

Line tools

The tools shown below allow you to draw straight or curved lines by clicking and dragging.

To create a curved line, select the Curve tool. Hold down the mouse button and drag out a straight line. Then click and drag the line at two points to create curves.

You can use the Line tool to draw a straight line vertically, horizontally, or at a 45° angle, by holding down the Shift key as you drag.

 Line tool button

 Curve tool button

Text tool

You can add text to a picture using the Text tool. Select the tool and then click at the point where you want to position the text. A box containing a flashing cursor will appear. When you start typing, the text will appear in this box. Drag the border of the box to create more space.

Text tool button **A**

Use the Text toolbar, shown below, to alter the font, style and size of the text. If you can't see the toolbar, switch it on from the *View* menu.

Text toolbar

Other tools

Other useful tools in the *Paint* Toolbox are the Eraser tool and the Magnifier tool.

If you make a mistake when drawing, drag the Eraser tool over the area you want to erase. It shades over the area with the background colour that is selected.

The Magnifier tool allows you to look at an area in more detail. When you select it, a rectangle will appear. Position it over the area of your picture that you want to magnify and click with the mouse button. This zooms in on the selected area. You can zoom back out by selecting the Magnifier tool again and clicking anywhere on the page.

Eraser tool button

Magnifier tool button

Practise painting

Try using *Paint* to create a picture to go with the invitation that you created using the *WordPad* program. You can find out how to put the two together on page 20.

Painting your own picture

Use the Rectangle tool to create box-shaped presents.

Use the Fill tool to colour in shapes.

The Airbrush tool creates this fuzzy effect.

Use the Polygon tool to create unusual shapes.

Save it!

Use the *Save As* command to save your picture (see page 16). Name it **My Picture** and save it in the Windows folder.

Images and objects

You can move and copy a section of a picture, called an image, within the *Paint* program using the cut and paste method you used in *WordPad* (see page 13). You can also combine work created in different programs. For example, you can add a picture created in *Paint* to a *WordPad* document. A file added in this way is called an object.

Selection tools

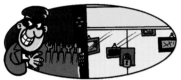

Before you can move, copy or delete an area of your *Paint* picture, you need to select it. You do this using the tools shown below.

Rectangle Selection tool   **Freeform Selection tool**

To use the Rectangle Selection tool, hold down the mouse button and drag a box around the area of your picture you want to select.

You can use the Freeform Selection tool to select an irregularly shaped area of your picture. Hold down the mouse button and draw around the area you want to select with the solid black line. When you release the mouse button, the shape will change to a dotted rectangle. However, it is still the irregular shape that is selected.

Moving pictures

To move a selected shape within a *Paint* picture, hold down the left mouse button while you drag it.

You can make a copy of a selected shape by holding down the Ctrl key as well as the mouse button. This leaves the original picture in place, but allows you to move a copy of it.

Mirror image

The *Image* menu in *Paint* contains options which allow you to turn sections of your picture around, or flip them over.

To use an *Image* command, select the area of the picture you want to alter. Then choose a command from the *Image* menu.

This picture shows the effects some of the Image *commands have.*

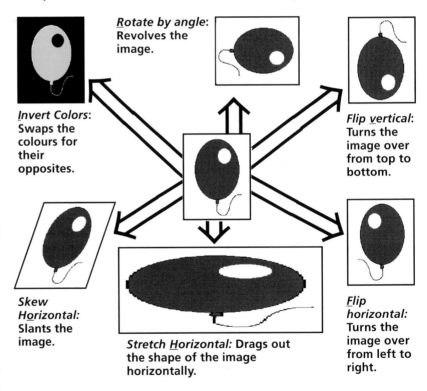

Rotate by angle: Revolves the image.

Invert Colors: Swaps the colours for their opposites.

Flip vertical: Turns the image over from top to bottom.

Skew Horizontal: Slants the image.

Stretch Horizontal: Drags out the shape of the image horizontally.

Flip horizontal: Turns the image over from left to right.

About objects

You can easily combine work created in different programs by inserting a file created in one program into a file created in a different program. An inserted file is called an object. An object can be text, pictures or even a sound or video file.

Windows 95 offers several different ways of inserting an object into a file.

Pasting between programs

The easiest way of moving sections of pictures or text between files in different programs is by using the *Copy* and *Paste* commands.

Try pasting the picture you created in *Paint* into WordPad Invitation. Open the My Picture file (in the Windows folder on the C drive). Use a selection tool to select the area you want to copy and select *Copy* from the *Edit* menu.

Open WordPad Invitation (in the Windows folder on the C drive). Position the cursor where you want the picture to appear. (It is easiest to paste the picture on a line without any text.) Then select *Paste* from the *Edit* menu.

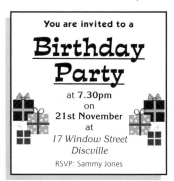

You are invited to a

Birthday
Party

at 7.30pm
on
21st November
at
17 Window Street
Discville
RSVP: Sammy Jones

You can use this technique to create a striking party invitation.

Working with objects

When you have pasted an object into a file, you can make changes to it by double-clicking on it. For example, double-click on the *Paint* object. A *Paint* window containing the picture will open. Make the alterations you want and then close the *Paint* window. Any changes will be shown on the picture in the *WordPad* document.

If you click on an object just once, a frame with eight handles appears around it. You can resize an object by clicking and dragging its handles. To move a framed object, hold down the mouse button and drag. The pointer changes to a pointer attached to a rectangle. Move it to where you want to position the picture and then release the mouse button.

You can also use the align buttons on the Format bar (see page 14) to position the picture in the middle, left, or right of the page.

A framed picture

A handle

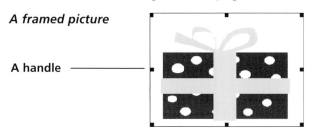

Object embedding

There are certain kinds of objects, such as sounds, that are best inserted into other files using a method called embedding.

To embed an object, open the file into which you want to insert the object. Then select *Object* from the *Insert* menu. In the *Insert Object* dialog box, select the *Create from File* option.

To locate the file you want to insert, click on the *Browse* button. In the *Browse* dialog box that appears, open the *Look in* drop-down list and click on the icon for the drive or folder where the file is stored. When you find the file's name, select it and click on the *Insert* button. This inserts the object into the file.

To make changes to an embedded object, use the same method as for a pasted object.

The Insert Object *dialog box*

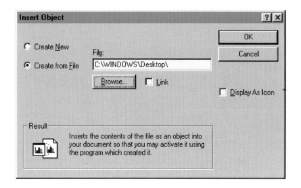

Object linking

You can use a method called linking to create a connection between an object and the file it came from. This means that whenever you make a change to the file and save it, the object will be changed too.

The link option is useful for objects that need to be updated. For example, you might want to use a table of figures created in *WordPad* in a leaflet created in *Paint*. If the object is linked, changing and saving the figures in one file will also change them in the other.

To link an object, follow the method for embedding an object, but make sure *Link* is selected in the *Insert Object* dialog box.

Multitasking and the Taskbar

Windows 95 has a feature called multitasking which allows you to do more than one job at the same time. When you are doing several jobs at once, you can use the Taskbar to help you to control the different windows that are open, and to keep your desktop organized.

The Taskbar

The main use of the Taskbar is to help you keep track of which programs are open on your desktop. Each program is represented by a button on the Taskbar, as shown on the big Taskbar running across the bottom of this page.

Switching windows

If you have several programs running at once, you can switch between them by clicking on the button on the Taskbar that represents the program you require.

It doesn't matter if you can't see a program's window. One click of its button will bring a window to the top of a pile of open windows, ready to use. This works for any program that is running, even if its window has been minimized.

Active windows

When there are several windows open on your desktop at once, the window that you are using is called an active window. It sits on top of all the other windows.

When a window is active, its button on the Taskbar looks different from the other buttons. It looks as though it has been pressed down. An active window usually has a different coloured Title bar from the other windows.

An active window sits on top of the other windows.

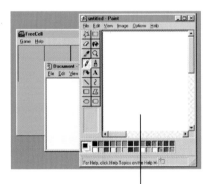

An active window

Tidying up

If you have several windows open on your desktop, it can look messy.

To tidy up any open windows, click on a blank part of the Taskbar with the right mouse button. From the menu that appears, choose *Cascade*. This arranges the windows so that they overlap one another neatly.

You can arrange windows side by side by choosing *Tile Horizontally* or *Tile Vertically*.

Cascaded windows

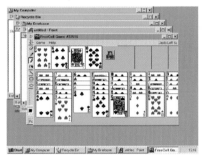

Windows tiled vertically

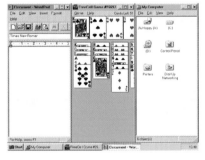

Closing

If you have finished using a program, you can close it down by clicking on its button on the Taskbar with the right mouse button. From the menu that appears, select *Close*.

The Taskbar   A program button

 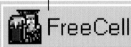 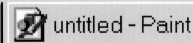 

Moving the Taskbar

The Taskbar is normally positioned along the bottom edge of your screen. However, you can move it so that it stretches along the top, left or right edge. To do this, point at a blank part of the Taskbar and, holding down the left mouse button, drag the Taskbar to a new location. When you release the mouse button, the Taskbar will cling to that edge of the screen.

Resizing the Taskbar

Sometimes, when you have lots of program windows open on your desktop, the Taskbar may become overcrowded. You can make room for the buttons and icons by making the Taskbar bigger.

To resize the Taskbar, move your pointer over its border. The pointer changes to a double-headed arrow. You can now drag the border until you have created enough space on the Taskbar. (You can only fill up to half of the screen with the Taskbar.)

Taskbar on top

The Taskbar is a very useful tool, so it's a good idea to make sure it is never covered up by the windows on your desktop.

To make sure the Taskbar always appears on top of everything else on your desktop, click on a blank part of the Taskbar with the right mouse button and select *Properties* from the menu that appears. In the *Taskbar Properties* dialog box, select the *Taskbar Options* tab. Switch on the *Always on top* option by clicking on it. A tick will appear in the box beside it.

When an option is switched on, a tick appears in its check box.

Hiding the Taskbar

When your desktop becomes crowded, you can make some extra space by hiding the Taskbar. To do this, select the *Auto hide* option on the

Taskbar Options property sheet. This makes the Taskbar disappear when it is not in use. It reappears when you use the pointer to touch the edge of the desktop where you left it.

Missing Taskbar?

If you can't find the Taskbar, hold down the Ctrl key and press Esc. It will reappear straight away.

Multitasking

Multitasking is a word used to describe what happens when a computer allows you to do more than one job, or task, at the same time.

Windows 95 has improved the way a computer uses its time. In previous versions of Windows, certain programs would sometimes prevent you from doing other things. Now it is much easier to do several things at once.

Multitasking is particularly useful when a computer is doing a job that takes a long time to complete, for example copying files or printing out documents. It means that you can do something else, such as writing a letter using *WordPad*, or playing a game, while the computer carries on with the job.

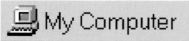

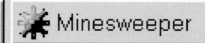

Files and folders

Whenever you save a document, such as a letter or a picture, it is stored as a file. Windows 95 has two programs, called *My Computer* and *Explorer*, which allow you to see what files you have stored on your computer.

My Computer

Launch *My Computer* by double-clicking on its icon on the desktop.

To make your display look similar to the one used on this page, check that the *Large Icons* option is selected on the *View* menu. Then, select *Options* from the *View* menu. In the *Options* dialog box, click on the *Folder* tab. Make sure the second option, shown below, is selected.

Choose this option to view the information in a single window.

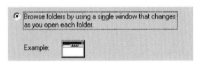

The *My Computer* window contains an icon for each of your disk drives. It may also have an icon for the *Control Panel* and your printer.

The My Computer window

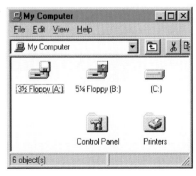

What's on *My Computer*?

To see what is stored on your C drive, double-click on its icon. The window changes to display the C drive's contents. It contains two different types of icons, one representing files, and the other representing files grouped together in folders.

The contents of the C drive

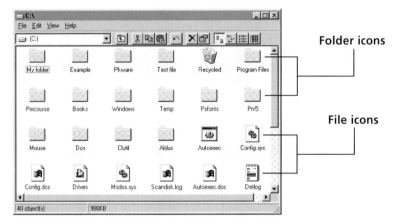

Folder icons

File icons

Folders

As you create more and more files, you should group them together so that they are easy to find. You can group files together in folders. For example, you could have one folder for work and another for home activities.

You can also have folders within folders. Any folder which is contained within another folder is called a sub-folder. For example, your home folder might have a sub-folder for letters.

Opening folders

To open a folder, double-click on its icon. For example, try opening the Windows folder on the C drive. The *My Computer* window will change to show its contents.

You can close a folder by clicking on the Up One Level button. This displays the contents of the previous folder or disk drive.

Up One Level button

Opening a file

You can open a file from the *My Computer* window by double-clicking on its icon. For example, try opening the file called WordPad Invitation that you created on page 15. It is stored in the Windows folder.

Explorer

The *Explorer* program offers an alternative way of looking at the information you viewed using *My Computer*. (*Explorer* replaces the Windows 3.1 program called *File Manager*.) Launch the *Explorer* program by clicking on its name on the *Programs* menu.

To make your display look similar to the one used on this page, open the *View* menu and check that the *Small Icons* option is selected. This reduces the size of the icons so that they can easily fit in the *Explorer* window.

Trees and branches

The *Explorer* window is divided into two parts. On the left-hand side, there are icons for your disk drives and some of the items on your desktop. These are displayed in a diagram that looks a bit like a tree, with lines like branches coming off a main trunk.

The Explorer *window*

The *My Computer* branch has smaller branches for the different disk drives.

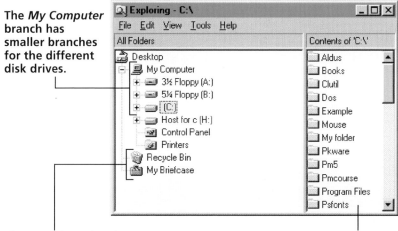

There are branches for some of the items on your desktop.

This side of the window shows the contents of the disk drive or folder highlighted on the left.

Exploring

To open a particular folder in *Explorer*, click on its name in the left-hand side of the window. For example, try opening the Windows folder. The folder icon changes to an open folder and its contents are displayed in the right-hand section of the window.

Branching out

A plus sign next to a folder tells you that it contains sub-folders. To see the sub-folders displayed as branches on the tree, click on the plus sign. It changes to a minus sign and a new set of branches is shown. Click on the minus sign to close the folder again.

If a folder doesn't have a plus or minus sign next to it, this means that it doesn't contain any sub-folders.

The diagram below shows a folder called Example on a branch off the C drive branch. Inside this folder are sub-folders named Home and Work. The Home folder branch has branches, representing sub-folders, for different kinds of home activities.

A section of the Explorer *window*

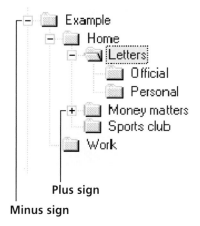

Plus sign

Minus sign

Opening a file

To open a file from the *Explorer* program, simply double-click on its icon in the right-hand side of the window. Try opening WordPad Invitation.

Organizing your files

Create your own folders for storing any files you want to keep. It is easy to reorganize your files by moving and copying them using the *Explorer* program.

Creating a folder

Before you create a folder, you need to tell your computer where to put it. To do this, select the disk drive where you want the folder to be stored.

Try creating a folder on the C drive. Launch the *Explorer* program and click on the C drive icon on the tree diagram. Select *New* on the *File* menu and click on *Folder* on the menu that opens. A new folder will appear in the right-hand side of the window.

Beside the folder is a box with the words New Folder highlighted. When you type a name for the folder, it will appear in this box. For example, type the name **My Folder** and press the Return key. The folder will appear in the folder tree on the left.

 **New Folder icon**

Folders in folders

You can create sub-folders within a folder using the same method. Instead of selecting the C drive as you did above, select the folder in which you want the sub-folder to appear.

Moving a file

You can reorganize your files by moving them from one folder to another. To move a file, you simply drag its icon.

Try moving WordPad Invitation from the Windows folder to My Folder. First, find WordPad Invitation. It is stored in the Windows folder on your C drive.

You need to be able to see the destination to which you want to drag the file. Check that you can see My Folder in the left-hand side of the window. If you can't, use the scroll bar to look down the list of files and folders.

Drag WordPad Invitation's icon over the My Folder icon in the left-hand side of the window and drop it. The file has now been moved to My Folder.

Moving a file between folders

Copying a file

Sometimes you may want to copy a file, for example if you want to make changes to a file but still keep the original copy.

Try making a second copy of WordPad Invitation in the Windows folder from which you have just moved it. To do this,

click on the file's name with the right mouse button and click on *Copy* from the menu that appears. Now click on the Windows folder's icon with the right mouse button. From the menu that appears, click on *Paste* to copy the file into the Windows folder.

No entry

If you see this symbol when you drag an icon, it means that you can't drop the icon at that location.

No Entry symbol

My Computer

Copying onto a floppy disk

To copy a file onto a floppy disk, you use the same drag and drop technique that you used to move a file.

Try copying WordPad Invitation onto a floppy disk. To do this, find WordPad Invitation's icon in My Folder. Then make sure you can see the icon for your floppy disk drive in the left-hand side of the window. Now drag the file's icon over the floppy disk drive's icon and drop it.

If there is no disk in the disk drive, your computer will display a message telling you to insert one. When you have inserted a floppy disk, your computer will copy the file.

As a file is copied, you will see a picture of it flying between two folders.

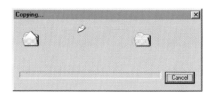

A new name

When you reorganize your files and folders, you may want to change their names. For example, when you have copied a file, you can give the second copy a different name so that you don't get the two confused.

Try changing the name of the copy of WordPad Invitation in the Windows folder. Find the icon of the file you want to rename and click on it with the right mouse button. Select *Rename* from the menu that appears. A box will appear around the name. Type **WordPad Copy** and press the Return key. The new name will replace the old one.

 Warning!
Only rename files and folders that you have created yourself. Renaming certain special Windows' files and folders could stop a program from working.

You can also use the *My Computer* program to create folders and to move or copy files between folders.

When creating a new folder, you need to tell your computer where to store it by clicking on a disk drive or folder icon. Then, in the same way as in the *Explorer* program, select *New* from the *File* menu and click on *Folder*. Type the name of the folder and then press the Return key.

To move a file or folder, click on its icon with the right mouse button. From the menu that appears, select *Cut* (or if you want to copy the item, select *Copy*). Click on the folder to which you want to move the item with the right mouse button and select *Paste* from the menu that appears. This moves (or copies) the file or folder to its new location.

Finding and deleting files

However well organized your filing system is, you may occasionally forget where you have put a file. Windows 95 has a program called *Find* to help you locate any lost files. To avoid cluttering up your hard disk, you should delete any files that you no longer need. You can do this using the *Explorer* and *My Computer* programs or by using a program called *Recycle Bin*.

Finding files

If you forget where you have stored a file, the *Find* program can help you to locate it again. Select *Find* from the Start menu and click on *Files or Folders* on the menu that opens.

Find icon

In the *Find* window, select the *Name & Location* tab. Enter the name of the file you are looking for in the *Named* box. Use the *Look in* drop-down list to tell your computer which disk drive to search. Click on the *Find Now* button to start the search. The names and locations of any matching files will be displayed in the box at the bottom of the window.

The Find *window*

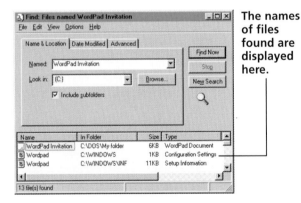

The names of files found are displayed here.

Forgotten a file's name?

If you don't know the name of the file you are looking for, but you know that the document contains a particular word, select the *Advanced* tab in the *Find* window. Enter the word in the *Containing text* box and select the type of file you are searching for from the *Of type* box. Then start the search as described above.

Deleting a file

You can delete a file using the *Explorer* or *My Computer* programs. Remind yourself how to use these programs on pages 24 and 25.

In *Explorer*, try deleting WordPad Copy from the Windows folder. In the left-hand side of the *Explorer* window, double-click on the C drive icon. Open the Windows folder and select WordPad Copy's icon. Then, select *Delete* from the *File* menu, or press the Delete key on your keyboard.

A dialog box may appear, asking you to confirm that you really want to delete the file. Check that the box contains the name and details of the file you want to delete. If it is correct, click on the *Yes* button.

You can delete whole folders using the same method. Be careful, though, because deleting a folder deletes all its contents.

Recycle Bin

Another way of getting rid of files is simply to throw them into the *Recycle Bin*. You'll find its icon on your desktop.

To use the *Recycle Bin*, you need to be able to see its icon. If you have any windows open on your desktop, you may need to minimize them, or drag them out of the way.

In *Explorer* or *My Computer*, click on the file you want to get rid of. Holding down the left mouse button, drag the file's icon over the *Recycle Bin* icon and drop it. The file icon will then disappear.

When you have thrown something into the *Recycle Bin*, its icon changes from an empty bin to a full one.

Recycle Bin *icons*

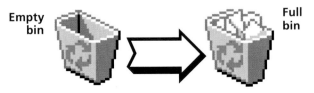

Empty bin   **Full bin**

Whoops!

If you accidentally delete something important, don't panic! Any files that you delete from your computer's hard disk are kept in the *Recycle Bin* for a while, which means that it's possible to get them back again.

To retrieve a file, double-click on the *Recycle Bin* icon. A list of deleted files will appear. Select the name of any file you want to retrieve and then select *Restore* from the *File* menu. The file will be transferred from the bin back to its original location. Alternatively, you can drag the file to a folder in the *Explorer* or *My Computer* window.

Unfortunately, this doesn't work for floppy disks. If you delete a file from a floppy disk, it's gone for good.

 ## Warning!

The *Recycle Bin* doesn't keep your files forever. Normally, Windows 95 starts to get rid of the oldest files for good when the deleted files take up more than 10% of your computer's hard disk.

Emptying the *Recycle Bin*

When you have dropped your files into the *Recycle Bin*, they still take up space on your hard disk. You can make more space by deleting the files once and for all. To do this, click on the *Recycle Bin* with the right mouse button and select *Empty Recycle Bin*. When the computer asks if you are sure, click on the *Yes* button. This will delete all the files in the *Recycle Bin* from the hard disk.

Grabbing groups

In *Explorer* and *My Computer*, you can select several files at once by holding down the Ctrl key and clicking on the files you want to select.

These highlighted files have been selected using the Ctrl key.

To select a group of files, click on the first file you want to grab and then press the Shift key while you click on the last file.

These files have been selected using the Shift key.

You can also use the mouse to grab a group of files. Position the pointer at one corner of the group of files you want to grab. Holding down the left mouse button, drag the mouse across until all the files you want are selected.

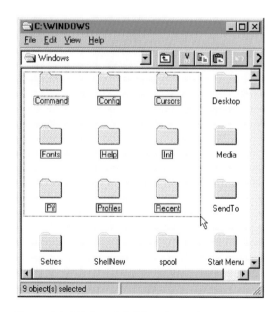

These highlighted folders have been selected using the click and drag method.

29

The personal touch

There are lots of changes you can make to Windows 95 to give it a more personal feel. In this section, you can find out how to change the colours and patterns used on your display. You can use passwords to help you customize Windows 95.

Making changes

You can make changes to Windows 95 using *Control Panel*. This is found in the *Settings* program group on the Start menu. *Control Panel* contains icons for the different aspects of your computer, such as the keyboard and mouse, that you can change.

You can change the way Windows 95 looks using the *Display Properties* box. Open this by double-clicking on the *Display* icon in the *Control Panel* window.

***Display* icon**

Find out about some of the practical changes you can make to the way Windows 95 works on page 42.

Take a shortcut

You can take a shortcut to the *Display Properties* box by clicking on a blank area of the desktop with the right mouse button and selecting *Properties* from the menu that appears.

Colour scheme

You can change the colours used for the desktop and for window parts such as the Title and Menu bars. You can choose from entire colour and design schemes, or create your own.

Select the *Appearance* tab in the *Display Properties* box. To choose an entire scheme, select a name from the *Scheme* list. The example display shows what the changes will look like.

To choose your own colours, select the part of the display you want to change from the *Item* list. Then choose a colour from the *Color* drop-down list. Click on *OK* when you have made your choices.

The Appearance *property sheet* in the Display Properties *box*

This example display shows how your choices will look.

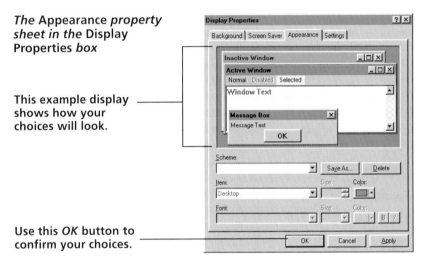

Use this *OK* button to confirm your choices.

Wallpaper

Brighten up your desktop by adding a patterned layer called wallpaper to it. Windows 95 has a selection of wallpaper designs to choose from. To look at them, select the *Background* tab in the *Display Properties* box. Click on a name from the *Wallpaper* list to see a design on the example screen.

Select *Tile* to make the wallpaper fill the desktop or *Center* to display just a square of wallpaper in the middle of the desktop.

When you have chosen the wallpaper you like, click on the *Apply* button and then click on *OK*. This puts the wallpaper on your desktop.

Clouds

Forest

Wallpaper designs

Screen savers

When you leave the same image on the screen for a long time, it can damage the screen by causing "screen burn". This means that the image is permanently imprinted on the screen.

Screen savers are programs which protect your screen by replacing the image with a moving picture after a certain amount of time.

Choosing a screen saver

Windows 95 provides a selection of screen savers from which you can choose. To have a look at the available screen savers, select the *Screen Saver* tab in the *Display Properties* box.

Open the drop-down list of screen savers and select one of them. A demonstration of what the screen saver looks like will appear on the example monitor. When you have chosen the one you want, click on the *OK* button.

An example monitor showing a screen saver called Flying Windows

Starting and stopping

When you have selected a screen saver, your computer will automatically start it if you haven't touched your keyboard or mouse for a certain amount of time.

You can alter the length of time your computer waits by changing the time in the *Wait* box at the bottom right of the *Screen Saver* box.

Once a screen saver has started, it will continue until you move your mouse or press a key on your keyboard.

About passwords

Sometimes, a computer is used by more than one person. Each person may want to customize Windows 95 in a different way.

If you share a computer, you can ensure that your chosen colours, patterns and other changes are switched on every time you use it by creating a password system.

Individual passwords

To create a password system, double-click on the *Passwords* icon in the *Control Panel*. This opens the *Passwords Properties* box. Click on the *User Profiles* tab and select the option *Users can customize their preferences...* Then click on *OK*.

Passwords icon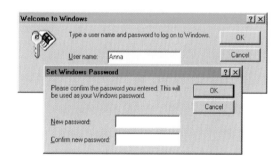

A box will appear asking whether you want to restart your computer. Click on the *Yes* button. When it has restarted, a box like the one below will appear. Enter your first name in the *User name* box. Then click in the *Password* box. Think of a password that you can easily remember and enter it here. Click on *OK*. A second box will appear, asking you to confirm the password you entered. Type the same password in the *Confirm new password* box and then click on *OK*.

These password boxes appear when you restart Windows 95.

When you have entered these details, a *Windows Networking* box will appear. Click on the *Yes* button to save your individual changes for future use.

Each time you start Windows 95, a password box will appear. When you enter your user name and password, any changes you have made will be activated.

Windows workshop

Windows 95 comes with a collection of programs that can help you to look after your computer. On these pages, you can find out how to use these programs. You'll also find out some ways of avoiding problems with your computer.

Spare copies

It's a good idea to keep spare copies of all your files, called backups, in case the original files get damaged or accidentally lost. The simplest way of doing this is by using the *Explorer* program to copy files onto floppy disks. You can remind yourself how to do this on page 27.

Multiple backups

If you have lots of files to back up, it is quicker to use a program called *Microsoft Backup*. *Microsoft Backup* is usually found on the *System Tools* menu in the *Accessories* program group. Launch it by clicking on its name.

In the *Microsoft Backup* window, select the *Backup* tab. It shows a similar structure to the one used in the *Explorer* window (see page 25). To look at the contents of a disk drive or folder, double-click on its icon.

The Microsoft Backup *window*

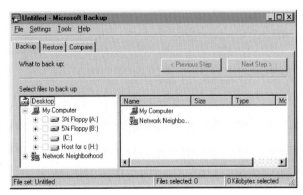

You can select which files or folders you want to back up by clicking on the check boxes to the left of their names. When you have selected the files, click on the *Next Step* button to choose where to store the backup.

Select the device to which you want to copy the files. You can use a floppy disk drive, but if you regularly back up lots of files, you might want to buy a device called a tape backup unit.

Click on *Start Backup.* The *Backup Set Label* box shown below will appear. Enter a name for the backup and click on *OK.* When the backup has been created, a message saying that the operation is complete will be displayed.

The Backup Set Label *dialog box*

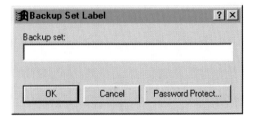

Restoring backups

If you lose or damage any files, you can get them back again, or restore them, from the backup you made. To do this, click on the *Restore* tab in the *Microsoft Backup* window. Insert the floppy disk or tape containing the backup. In the left side of the window, click on the icon for the disk or tape drive you are using. The backup's name will appear in the right side of the window. Click on it and then click on the *Next Step* button.

The window changes to show the contents of the backup. Click on the check boxes beside any files you want to restore and then click on the *Start Restore* button. The files will be returned to their original locations on your hard disk.

⚠️ **Warning!**

You should make backup copies of all the files you have created before using any of the programs on page 33.

Checking for damage

After a long period of time, parts of your computer's hard disk may wear out or become damaged. Windows 95 has a program called *ScanDisk* which you can use to check for any damage to the disk itself, or for any problems with the way your files are organized.

Launch *ScanDisk* from the *System Tools* menu in the *Accessories* program group. A window like the one below will appear. It contains a list of the disk drives that you can check for errors. Select the C drive.

There are two different kinds of check you can make: the *Standard* test and the *Thorough* test. The *Standard* test checks your files and folders. If you turn off your computer without closing down files properly, this can leave useless bits of files on your hard disk. When you run this test, it will clear these bits away.

The *Thorough* test scans the surface of the disk for errors. If there are any damaged areas, it tells Windows 95 not to use those areas when saving information or adding programs.

Select the test you want to use and then click on the *Start* button to set it going.

The ScanDisk *window*

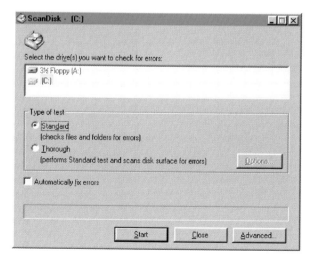

Hard disk order

When you store files on your hard disk, they are slotted in anywhere there is space. This can cause your hard disk to become disorganized. When this happens, it may take the computer longer to find things.

You can use a program called *Disk Defragmenter* to tidy up your hard disk. This gathers all the bits of each file together so that they can easily be found. You should use it once every three or four months to keep your hard disk in good order.

Disk Defragmenter is usually found on the *System Tools* menu in the *Accessories* program group. Click on its name to launch it. In the box that appears, select the C drive. A box like the one below will appear, telling you whether or not it needs defragmenting. If it does, click on *Start* to set it going. If not, click on *Exit*.

This box tells you whether to defragment the disk.

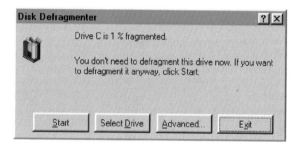

Shutting down Windows 95

When you have finished using your computer, you should instruct it to shut down Windows 95 before you turn it off. Switching off without doing this can damage your programs and files.

To shut down Windows 95 properly, select *Shut Down* from the Start menu. In the dialog box that appears select *Shut down the computer?* and click on the *Yes* button. If you have any document files open, you will be asked whether you want to save them.

Wait until a message appears saying that you can turn off your computer safely, then switch it off at the power button. There may be a separate switch to turn off your monitor.

Games and gadgets

The *Accessories* program group contains lots of useful programs. Here are some of the ones you haven't come across elsewhere in the book. You can also find out how to add any Windows 95 programs that aren't available on your computer.

Character Map

There are all kinds of arrows, mathematical symbols and other characters that you can use in Windows 95, but which don't appear on your keyboard. Use a program called *Character Map* to view all these different characters.

In the *Character Map* window, select a font from the drop-down list. The grid, or map, below it displays the characters available in that font. You can copy any of these characters to use in a document. To do this, select the character you want to copy by clicking on it. Then click on the *Select* button.

Character Map showing a font called Wingdings

The character will appear in the *Characters to Copy* box. Repeat this process to select more characters.

When you have selected all the characters you want, click on the *Copy* button. This copies all the characters in the *Characters to Copy* box onto the Clipboard.

Open the file in which you want to insert the characters and position the cursor where you want them to appear. Select *Paste* from the *Edit* menu to add the characters to the document.

Notepad

As well as *WordPad* (see page 12), Windows 95 has another word processing program called *Notepad*. *Notepad* is a useful program because, when you launch it, its window appears very quickly. This means that it is handy for simple documents, or for jotting down notes or a shopping list. However, you can't insert pictures into a *Notepad* document or use different fonts and text styles.

Calculator

Windows 95 has its own handy calculator. To launch *Calculator*, click on its name on the *Accessories* menu.

The window that opens contains a picture of a calculator. To use it, click on its buttons using your mouse, or use the keys on your keyboard to enter information.

A Standard *calculator*

You can choose between a simple calculator (*Standard*) and one which can be used for more complicated calculations (*Scientific*). These options are available on the *View* menu.

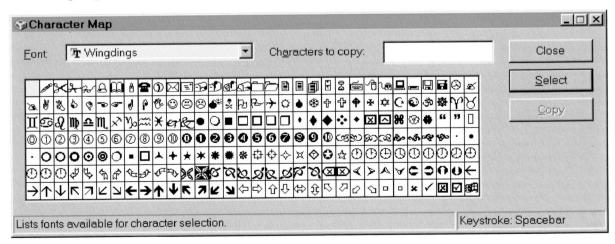

Games

The Windows 95 package contains several simple games programs. They are usually grouped together on the *Games* menu, which opens from the *Accessories* menu.

You can find out how to play a game by selecting *Help Topics* from its *Help* menu (see page 44). The help topics explain the rules and give advice on how to play. To start a game, select *New* on the *Game* menu.

Windows 95 games

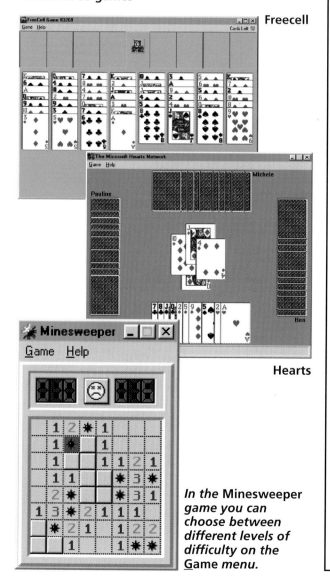

Freecell

Hearts

In the Minesweeper *game you can choose between different levels of difficulty on the* Game *menu.*

Adding programs

If there are programs in this book that aren't available on your computer, you can easily add, or "install", them.

To install a program, click on the *Add/ Remove Programs* icon in the *Control Panel*. Select the *Windows Setup* tab. This lists all the programs and devices, called components, that are available with Windows 95. The items with ticks beside their names are those that have already been installed on your computer.

The Add/Remove Programs Properties *box*

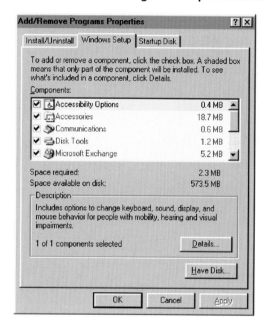

Certain items on the list represent program groups. When you select one of these, the *Description* box indicates how many other items it contains, and how many of these have been installed. Click on the *Details* button to see the list.

To install a component, click in the check box beside its name and click on the *Apply* button. You will then be asked to insert a CD or floppy disk with the program on it. This refers to the disks on which your Windows 95 software was supplied. Follow the instructions as they appear on your screen. You may need to restart Windows 95 before some changes will take effect.

Getting connected

If you work on more than one computer, you can use a program called *My Briefcase* to transfer information between computers. You can also connect computers so that they can share equipment and exchange information. When two or more computers are connected, they form a group called a network. A program called *Network Neighborhood* can help you to work with a network.

My Briefcase

The *My Briefcase* program offers a simple way of transferring files between computers that aren't connected. You can work on one computer and then use *My Briefcase* to "carry" your files to another computer. This can be useful if you have a computer at home and one at work or school, or if you use a laptop computer.

You will find the *My Briefcase* icon on your desktop.

My Briefcase icon

Using *My Briefcase*

To copy a file or folder into *My Briefcase*, simply drag its icon from the *Explorer* or *My Computer* window to the *My Briefcase* icon and then drop it. To transport the files, insert a floppy disk into your disk drive and click on the *My Briefcase* icon with the right mouse button. From the menu that appears, select *Send To* and then select the floppy drive. The *My Briefcase* icon will disappear from your desktop as it is moved to the floppy disk.

My Briefcase update

When you use another computer, it is easiest to leave the files on floppy disk while you work on them. To do this, insert the disk and click on the floppy disk drive icon in the *Explorer* window. Then double-click on the *My Briefcase* icon. You can open a file by double-clicking on its icon. Remember to save any changes you make onto the floppy disk.

When you next use your main computer, insert the disk containing *My Briefcase*. In the *Explorer* window, click on the floppy disk drive icon and then double-click on the *My Briefcase* icon. Select *Update All* from the *Briefcase* menu. A dialog box will appear telling you which files have been changed. Click on the *Update* button to update the changed files.

The **Update My Briefcase** *dialog box*

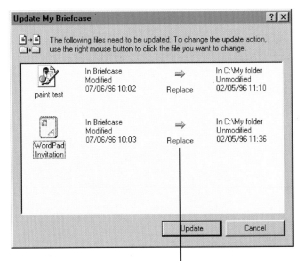

The symbol in this column shows what will happen when you update the files. For example, here the files on the left will replace the files on the right.

Connecting computers

Computers in the same office can be connected using special cables. Over greater distances you can connect them using the telephone system and a device called a modem. A modem translates computer information so that it can be sent via the telephone line. This enables you to connect with computers all over the world.

Network Neighborhood

If your computer is part of a network, your desktop will contain an icon for the *Network Neighborhood* program. Double-click on it to launch the program.

Network Neighborhood allows you to see which other computers are connected to your computer, although it only shows those computers that are switched on.

Network Neighborhood

Network Neighborhood icon

Workgroups

In a large network, users may be divided into groups called workgroups. A workgroup might consist of people who work in the same room or who do the same type of job. This means that files or equipment can be shared just between the members of a particular workgroup, rather than everybody on the network. Each workgroup and computer will be given a name so that it can be identified easily on the network. For example, a computer might be identified by its user's name.

In the *Network Neighborhood* window, click on the *Entire Network* icon to see a list of the workgroups on your network. Double-click on a workgroup name to see a list of the computers in that workgroup.

The **Network Neighborhood** *window*

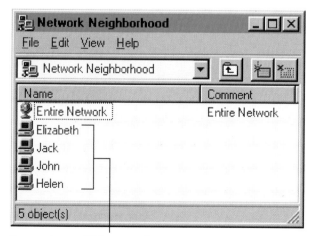

Computers within a workgroup

Sharing and using

The advantage of being on a network is that you can share facilities with other network users. However, nobody on your network can use the equipment and folders on your computer until you have told it to "share" them.

Sharing a folder

To share a folder with the other computer users on your network, find the folder you want to share in the *My Computer* window. Click on its icon with the right mouse button. From the menu that appears, click on *Sharing*.

In the dialog box that appears, select the *Sharing* tab. Then select the *Shared As* option. You can restrict what other computer users can do to a shared folder. If you choose *Read-Only*, this means that other users can only look at your folder, but can't make any changes to it. *Full* access means that other network users can change the folder. When you have told your computer to share a folder, its icon in the *My Computer* window will change to a folder being offered by a hand. You can share printers and CD drives using the same method.

My Shared Folder

A shared folder icon

Opening shared folders

Once a folder has been shared, any of the network users can open the shared folder just as if it was on their own computer.

The *Network Neighborhood* window works in a similar way to the *My Computer* window (see page 24), but it allows you to explore what is on the other computers on your network as well as your own. To see what is stored on another computer on your network, double-click on its icon. You can open shared folders in the same way. To open and use a document in a shared folder, double-click on its icon.

The *Microsoft Network*

The *Microsoft Network* enables you to link up with other computers. You can use it to send messages and to exchange information on all kinds of subjects. It also gives you access to the Internet, a huge network which links computers all over the world.

Joining the *Microsoft Network*

Before you can use the *Microsoft Network*, you need a modem (see page 36). You also need to join the *Microsoft Network*. There may be a free trial period of membership, but after this you will have to pay to use it. To join the *Microsoft Network*, double-click on its icon on your desktop and follow the instructions below.

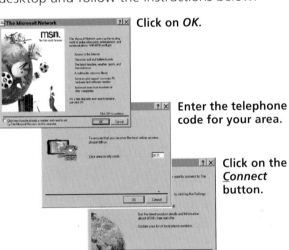

Click on *OK*.

Enter the telephone code for your area.

Click on the *Connect* button.

Click on each of the three icons in turn to give the information required to join. (This includes details of how you will pay.) Then click on the *Join Now* button.

You will need to choose a Member ID and a password. Your Member ID is the name by which you would like to be known when you use the *Microsoft Network*. You enter this information in the *Sign in* box each time you connect to the *Microsoft Network*.

Using the *Microsoft Network*

The first page that you will see on the *Microsoft Network* is *Microsoft Today*. This contains information about the latest things happening on the *Microsoft Network*. When you move your pointer over certain pictures or words on the screen, it changes to a hand pointer. This means that you can click for more information.

Close the *Microsoft Today* window. You will now see the *Microsoft Network (MSN) Central* page. This is the page you will use to start exploring the *Microsoft Network*.

The MSN Central *page*

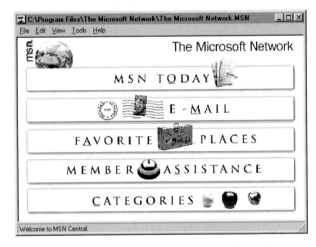

Finding your way around

Click on *Member Assistance* on the *MSN Central* page. This contains information that will help you to find your way around the *Microsoft Network*. Try double-clicking on the *Welcome!* icon to find out how to get started.

To get back to the *MSN Central* page, click on the *Microsoft Network* icon on the Taskbar with the right mouse button and select *Go to MSN Central*. Click on *Categories* to see the kinds of subjects you can find out about. There are lots of pages, called sites, for you to look at. Double-click on the subject icons to see more information.

About e-mail

Once you have joined the *Microsoft Network*, you can use a program called *Microsoft Exchange* to send electronic mail, or e-mail. E-mail is a quick way of communicating with people all over the world.

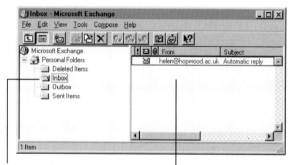

Before you can send a message to someone, you need to know their e-mail address. Everyone who is on the *Microsoft Network* or the Internet will have one of these. Here is an imaginary *Microsoft Network* address:

membername@msn.com

Sending messages

You can launch *Microsoft Exchange* by clicking on its name on the *Programs* menu, or by selecting e-*mail* in the *MSN Central* window. In the *Microsoft Exchange* window, click on the *New Message* button. This opens a *New Message* window.

New Message button

Enter the e-mail address to which you want to send a message in the *To* box. Then type a short description of what the message is about in the *Subject* box. Click on the blank page area to enter your message. When you have finished, click on the *Send* button to deliver it. A message will appear at the bottom of the window to indicate that your e-mail is being sent.

Send button

A New Message *window*

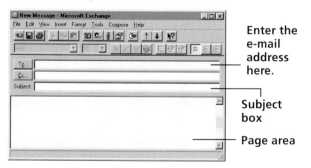

Enter the e-mail address here.

Subject box

Page area

Reading mail

When you connect to the *Microsoft Network*, a message appears if you have received new mail. Any e-mail you receive is stored in the *Inbox* folder until you have read it.

To read a message, select e-*mail* in the *Microsoft Central* window. In the *Microsoft Exchange* window, double-click on Personal Folders in the left side of the window and then double-click on the Inbox folder. Any new mail is listed on the right side of the window. Double-click on an item to read the message.

The Microsoft Exchange Inbox *window*

Inbox folder   Any new mail is listed here.

The Internet

The Internet offers another way of connecting up with other computers. You can join news and discussion groups and use a facility called the World Wide Web to look up information stored on computers all over the world.

You will need a program called *Internet Explorer* to find your way around the Internet. You can get an up-to-date copy of this from the *Microsoft Network*. To do this, click on *Categories* on the *MSN Central* page. Double-click on the *Internet Centre* folder and then double-click on the *Getting on the Internet* icon. Follow the instructions provided on that page. It takes about half an hour to copy it onto your computer.

When the process is complete, an *Internet Explorer* icon will appear on your desktop. Double-click on this and follow the instructions to find out how to get started on the Internet.

Discovering multimedia

Computers can be used to combine text, sound, pictures and video. This is called multimedia. Windows 95 has several multimedia programs. These are usually found on the *Multimedia* menu in the *Accessories* program group. Find out what equipment you need to make the most of multimedia in the Equipment box below.

About CD-ROMs

All kinds of games and information programs use multimedia. Multimedia software is usually available on CD-ROM, a kind of disk that stores large amounts of information. You will need a device called a CD-ROM drive to play one of these.

Multimedia CD-ROMS allow you to listen to sound clips and watch video clips as well as read text. Many CD-ROMs are interactive. This means that you can click on the screen to make things happen.

A screen from a multimedia CD-ROM

The procedure that you need to follow in order to use CD-ROMs can vary. You will need to follow the instructions provided with each one to find out what to do.

CD Player

You can use your CD-ROM drive to play music CDs while you work on your computer. The *CD Player* program allows you to control what's playing. It has buttons which work like those on an ordinary CD player.

To play a CD, insert it into the CD-ROM drive and launch *CD Player.* Click on the Play button to start the CD playing.

The CD Player *window*

Play button

Equipment

Before you can work with sound and video you need special equipment, or "hardware". Some computers, called multimedia computers, already have everything that you will need. If you don't have one of these, you can add hardware onto your computer.

To try out the programs in this section, you will need a sound card, a fast graphics card, a CD-ROM drive, a microphone and some headphones or speakers. Ask at a good computer shop for advice on buying and adding hardware.

Plug and Play

Windows 95 has a feature called Plug and Play. This means that it automatically checks for new hardware and arranges your computer system so that it can work properly. If you have a Plug and Play computer, this makes adding hardware very easy. When you buy hardware, you should check that it is suitable for a Plug and Play system.

A multimedia computer

Media Player

If your computer has a sound card and a fast graphics card, you can play sound and video files using a program called *Media Player*.

If your Windows 95 software is on CD-ROM, you will have several sample files. To play one of these, launch *Media Player* and select <u>O</u>pen from the <u>F</u>ile menu. Open the Media folder (in the Windows folder on the C drive). Select *All files* in the *Files of <u>t</u>ype* box. A list of the files will be displayed. Select one and click on <u>O</u>pen.

The *Media Player* window contains buttons similar to those found on ordinary CD and tape players. Click on these to play your selected file.

The Media Player *window*

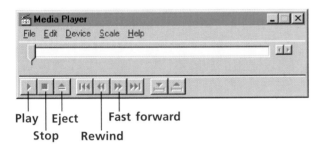

Play | Eject | Fast forward
Stop | Rewind

Recording sounds

If you have a microphone attached to your computer, you can use *Sound Recorder* to record your own sounds. Launch *Sound Recorder* from the *Multimedia* menu.

Try recording your voice. Click on the Record button and speak into the microphone. Click on the Stop button to stop the recording. To save the file, select *Save <u>A</u>s* from the <u>F</u>ile menu. Give it a name and save it in the Media folder.

The Sound Recorder *window*

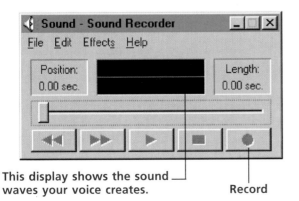

This display shows the sound waves your voice creates.   Record

Sound effects

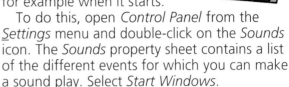

You can instruct your computer to play a sound when a particular thing happens in Windows 95, for example when it starts.

To do this, open *Control Panel* from the <u>S</u>ettings menu and double-click on the *Sounds* icon. The *Sounds* property sheet contains a list of the different events for which you can make a sound play. Select *Start Windows*.

The CD-ROM version of Windows 95 has several prerecorded sounds. Select one of these from the <u>N</u>ame drop-down list. To hear it, click on the Play button. Click on *OK* when you have found the sound you want to use. Your chosen sound will now play each time you start Windows 95. You can also use sounds that you have recorded yourself.

The Sounds Properties *dialog box*

A drop-down list of available sounds   Events for which you can play a sound

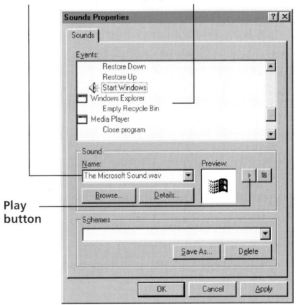

Play button

Volume Control

You can control the volume and quality of sound produced by your computer using a program called *Volume Control.* You can launch this from the *Multimedia* menu, or by double-clicking on the Speaker icon at the end of the Taskbar.

Tips and tricks

Here are some tips to help make Windows 95 easier to use. You can use the *Control Panel* to customize Windows 95 in lots of useful ways. You can also find out about shortcuts and other handy tricks.

Mouse buttons

If you are left-handed, you may find the mouse awkward to use. Windows 95 allows you to change the way it works so that it suits you. To do this, open the *Control Panel* window from the *Settings* menu and double-click on the *Mouse* icon. In the *Mouse Properties* dialog box, click on the *Buttons* tab.

Choose between a left-handed and a right-handed mouse by clicking on the appropriate option button. The example mouse picture shows the effect that each button will have.

If you do alter your mouse, remember that all the instructions in this book are for a right-handed mouse arrangement.

An example mouse shows what the buttons do.

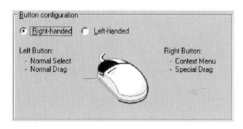

Double-click trouble

If your computer doesn't always respond when you double-click, this may be because you are not clicking quickly enough.

To change the double-click speed, click on the *Buttons* tab in the *Mouse Properties* box.

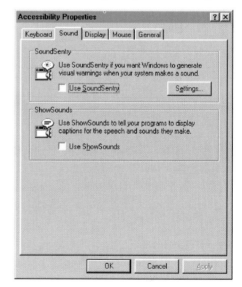

This contains a slide which you can use to adjust the speed. Slow down the double-click speed by dragging the slide to the left. This increases the amount of time that is allowed to pass between your clicks.

You can try out the new speed by double-clicking in the test area. Each time you double-click successfully, the jack-in-a-box will pop in or out of its box.

Drag the slide to change the double-click speed.

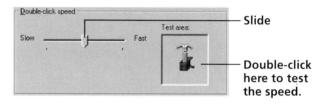

- Slide
- Double-click here to test the speed.

Accessibility

Windows 95 has a feature called *Accessibility Options*. This is designed to make Windows 95 easier to use for people who have hearing or sight problems, or who have difficulty using a keyboard or mouse.

Double-click on the *Accessibility Options* icon in the *Control Panel* window to see the changes you can make. Select an option by clicking on its check box.

The Accessibility Properties *dialog box*

You can make all kinds of useful changes. For example, for people with hearing difficulties the *Sound* property sheet has options for Windows 95 to display captions or visual warnings when your computer makes a noise.

Program shortcuts

If you use a particular program regularly, you might want to create a shortcut to it on your desktop. The easiest way of doing this is to drag the program's icon onto the desktop.

Try creating a shortcut for the game program called *Freecell*. In *Explorer*, open the Windows folder and find the *Freecell* icon. Make sure that you can see the desktop and then click on the icon with the left mouse button. Hold down the mouse button while you drag the icon onto the desktop. When you drop the icon, a small arrow and a shortcut title are added.

You can start a program from its shortcut icon by double-clicking on it.

***Freecell* shortcut**

The StartUp folder

Windows 95 has a folder called the StartUp folder where you can put programs and files that you want to launch automatically each time you start Windows 95. For example, you could put a useful program such as *Scandisk* (see page 33) in the StartUp folder, so that it is ready to use when you start Windows 95.

To add a program to the StartUp folder, open the *Explorer* window and find the name of the program you want to add. Make sure you can see the StartUp folder in the left side of the window. It is usually stored in the *Programs* folder in the Windows folder. Then drag the program's icon over the StartUp folder and drop it. The program will now be launched each time you start Windows 95.

You can easily delete any shortcuts that you make. Simply click on the shortcut icon with the right mouse button and select *Delete* from the menu that appears.

Clock

A clock is displayed at the end of the Taskbar. To look at the date, place your pointer over the clock. After a few seconds, a box containing the date will appear. Check that the correct time and date are shown. Your files are stamped with this information so that they are easy to find and organize. This is only useful if the information is correct.

To alter the time or date, click on the clock with the right mouse button and select *Adjust Date/Time* from the menu that appears. A dialog box like the one below will appear. Click on the *Date & Time* tab and make any corrections.

The Date/Time Properties *dialog box*

Change the month in this box.　**Click on the arrows to change the year.**

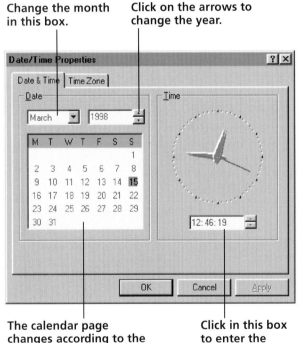

The calendar page changes according to the month that is selected.　**Click in this box to enter the correct time.**

Documents folder

The *Documents* folder on the Start menu contains a list of the last 15 documents on which you worked. You can use it as a quick way of opening a document you used recently. Double-click on a document's name to open it.

There are some programs which can't add files to the *Documents* folder. If you use a file from one of these programs, its name won't appear on the *Documents* menu.

Help!

Windows 95 has its own built-in help system. You can use it to find out how Windows 95 works, to get more information about a difficult term, or just to refresh your memory.

Starting *Help*

To open the *Help* system, click on the Start button and then click on *Help*. The *Help Topics* window will appear on your desktop. It contains three property sheets marked *Contents*, *Index* and *Find*.

Contents

The *Contents* section contains a general index of information organized by subject, like the contents page of a book.

Next to each item in the index is a picture of a book. Each book represents a main subject area. Double-click on a book to see more subjects within that subject area. You can close a book again by double-clicking on it.

The Contents *property sheet*

Try opening the *How To...* book by double-clicking on it and then open the *Work with Files and Folders* book. This displays a list of topics providing useful tips on using files and folders.

The topics have question marks next to them. When you double-click on one of these, a topic window with step-by-step information on that subject will be displayed.

A topic window provides information on a specific subject area.

Index

The *Index* section has more topics than the *Contents* section and its subjects are arranged in alphabetical order.

To find a particular topic, type the word that you are looking for into the first box. For example, try typing **file**. The matching part of the index will appear in the box below.

Use the scroll bar to look through the list. When you see a topic you want to know more about, double-click on it to open its window.

Warning!

Closing a topic window takes you out of the entire *Help* system. If you want to return to the main *Help* system, click on the *Help Topics* button.

Starting *Find*

The *Find* section enables you to carry out a more general search for help by looking for words or phrases within a topic window. This is useful if you can't find what you are looking for in the other sections.

When you click on the *Find* tab, a box like the one below may appear. This means that the computer needs to create a word list before you can use the *Find* facility. Select *Minimize Database size* and click on the *Next* button. Then click on the *Finish* button. This creates a list of all the words used in the *Help* system.

This screen appears if you need to create a list of words.

Using *Find*

When a word list has been created, the *Find* property sheet will be displayed.

The **Find** *property sheet*

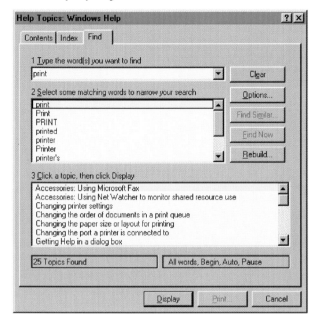

Type the word you are looking for in the first box. For example, try typing **print**. Any words in the word list that match what you have typed, for example print, printing and printer, will be displayed in the box below. If the box is blank, this means that no match has been found.

If there is a list of words in the second box, click on the one you want to know more about. For example, try clicking on **print**. A list of the topics that contain the word print will appear in the third box. Double-click on a topic to see its window.

Help gadgets

Some topic windows have gadgets to help you find your way around the *Help* system. The window below shows some of these devices.

A topic window

Click on a button like this to take a shortcut to the box or window named.

Click on any word underlined with a dotted line to see an explanation of what the word means.

Click on a box like this to see a list of similar subjects.

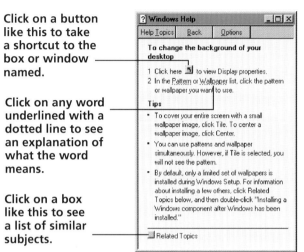

What's This?

Most Windows dialog boxes have a built-in *Help* facility called *What's This?*. It enables you to find out about certain features in a particular box. To use *What's This?*, click on the question mark button in the top right corner of the dialog box. The pointer will change to a pointer attached to a question mark.

To find out about an item in a dialog box, move the pointer over the item and click on it. A short description of what it does will appear. Click elsewhere in the dialog box to get rid of the explanation.

A *What's This?* button

Windows 95 tour

Windows 95 has its own "tour" which gives you a hands-on guide to using Windows. To start the tour, click on the *Contents* tab in the *Help* system and double-click on *Ten minutes to using Windows*.

Guide to differences

If you've used Windows before, you may find it difficult to get used to some of the differences between Windows 95 and Windows 3.1. This chart guides you through some of the main ones. You can look up a particular task and see how it was carried out in Windows 3.1 and then find out the new way of doing it in Windows 95.

Task	Windows 3.1	Windows 95
Program organization	*Program Manager* gathered together all your programs in program groups.	Your program groups are shown as folders on the *Programs* menu on the Start menu (see page 8).
Launching programs	Programs were launched using *Program Manager* or *File Manager*.	You can launch a program by clicking on its name on the *Programs* menu (see page 8).
Organizing files	*File Manager* enabled you to see what was on your computer and to move, copy and delete files.	*Explorer* works in a similar way to *File Manager*. You can also use *My Computer* to work with files. (See pages 24-9).
Finding files	In *File Manager*, you used the *Search* command on the *File* menu to look for missing files.	The *Find* program allows you to carry out more complicated searches (see page 28).
Deleting files	Files were deleted in *File Manager* using the Delete command or key.	Files can be deleted in *Explorer* or *My Computer* or using *Recycle Bin* (see pages 28-9). *Recycle Bin* also allows you to "undelete" files.
Naming files	File names could only have eight characters.	File names can have up to 255 characters (see page 16).
Switching between program windows	You could use the Alt and Tab keys or the Ctrl and Esc keys to switch between windows.	As well as using these keys, you can also use the Taskbar to switch between windows (see page 22).
Making use of the desktop	The desktop was only used for minimized program icons.	The desktop contains icons for several programs (see page 4). You can also add your own shortcut icons (see page 43).
Selecting options in a dialog box	Selected options were marked with a cross.	Selected options are marked with a tick (see page 11).
Closing a window	Windows were closed using the *Exit* command on the *File* menu or by selecting *Close* from the Control menu.	You can also close a window by clicking on its Close button (see page 9).
Using programs	You used the *Write* program to work with text and the *Paintbrush* program for drawing pictures.	The word processing program is called *WordPad* and the drawing program is called *Paint* (see pages 12-15 and 18-19).

Index

Windows 95 screenshots, icons, and box shot (page 3) reprinted with permission from Microsoft Corporation.
Microsoft® Natural® keyboard, cover; Microsoft® mouse, pages 3 and 6: photographs used with permission from
Microsoft Corporation. Microsoft and Microsoft Windows are registered trademarks of Microsoft Corporation in
the US and other countries.
Laptop computer, page 6: photograph by permission of Olivetti Personal Computers.
Multimedia PC, page 40: photograph reproduced with the permission of Gateway 2000.
Usborne "Exploring Nature" CD-ROM, page 40: Main Multimedia.